LUNA LUCY & THE PLANETS

by Lisa Van Der Wielen

Illustrated by Joseph Hopkins

For Eva & Mia

Shoot for the stars

Lisa Van Der Wielen

ABOUT THE AUTHOR

Lisa Van Der Wielen is a primary school teacher and writer from Perth, Western Australia. Her passions for teaching and writing lead her to become a Children's Author with her first picture book being published in 2017. Her books; Vegetarian Polony, Luna Lucy, Aqua Dog and The Life of Gus support the charities Perth Children's Hospital Foundation and Ronald McDonald House. Her love for the beach, nature, dogs, family and the importance of virtues provide her with inspiration to write poetry and stories that inspire.

www.lisavanderwielen.com

LUNA LUCY & THE PLANETS

First published November 2020

LUNA LUCY & THE PLANETS

One stormy day, with little to do,
Lucy built a rocket ship, with boxes and glue.

"We're going on an adventure!" said Lucy to Neptune.
"First stop will be the pearly white moon!"

The moon sky was bouncy; they floated in the air.
All they could see was white dust everywhere.

"Next stop is Mercury," Lucy did say.
The smallest planet looks a dusty dark grey.

With extreme temperatures, both very hot and cold.
It zips 'round the sun with a speed to behold.

With only 88 days to orbit the sun,
The speed of Mercury can't be outdone.

With a giant iron core right in the centre,
Mercury would be impossible to enter.

"Next stop is Venus," Lucy said to her dog.
With volcanoes and heat and air full of fog.

Venus has phases just like the moon.
It's the brightest of planets, even at noon.

But Venus and Mercury have no moon at all.
Nothing that orbits them, not even small.

Next is our planet, the sphere we call Earth.
With water and oxygen, a planet of birth.

Earth is the planet third from the sun.
Twenty-four hours and a day is done!

"Next stop: the red planet. Off we go to Mars!"
Said Luna Lucy as they zoomed through the stars.

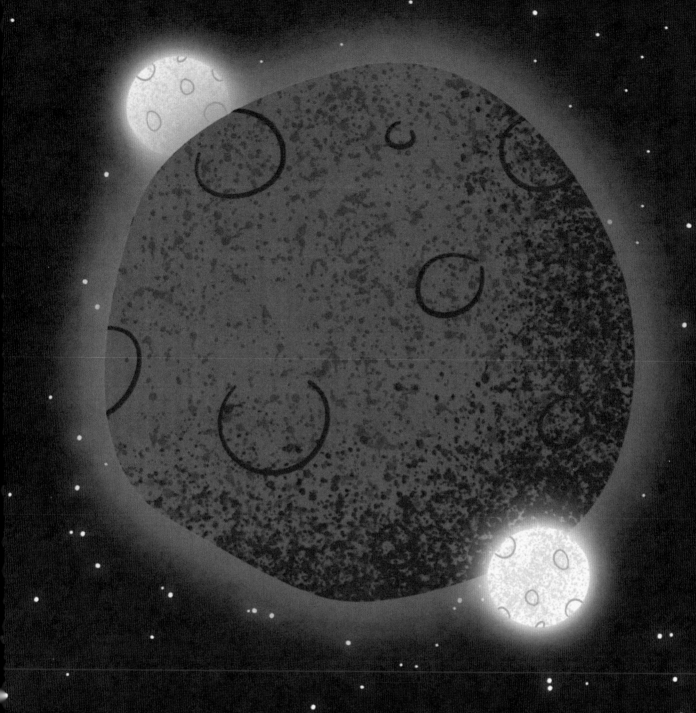

Mars looks red, with north and south poles.
With seasons like Earth and craters and holes.

It's a rocky planet with two small moons.
Huge, hot volcanoes that spread like monsoons.

Lucy said: "Next is Jupiter, that big stripey ball.
I bet that it's the biggest planet of all!"

Covered in clouds; brown, red, yellow and white.
These make the atmosphere an interesting sight.

WOOF! WOOF!

Jupiter's dark red spot is a gigantic storm.
With winds oh so strong and so very warm.

The great big red spot is much bigger than Earth –
Seventy-nine moons are what Jupiter's worth.

"Off to Saturn!" Lucy began to sing.
"It's the planet with a colourful ring!"

JANUARY | Enero • Janvier

2021

SUNDAY Dom • Dim	MONDAY Lun • Lun	TUESDAY Mar • Mar	WEDNESDAY Mié • Mer	THURSDAY Jue • Jeu	FRIDAY Vie • Jeu	SATURDAY Sáb • Sam
					1 New Year's Day	2
3	4	5	6	7	8	9
10	11	12	13	14	15	16
17	18	19	20	21	22	23
24	25 Martin L. King Jr (US)	26	27	28	29	30
31						

Febrero • February • Février

S	M	T	W	T	F	S
	1	2	3	4	5	6
7	8	9	10	11	12	13
14	15	16	17	18	19	20
21	22	23	24	25	26	27
28						

Notes • Notas • Remarques

2021

FEBRUARY | Febrero • Février

SUNDAY Dom • Dim	MONDAY Lun • Lun	TUESDAY Mar • Mar	WEDNESDAY Mié • Mer	THURSDAY Jue • Jeu	FRIDAY Vie • Jeu	SATURDAY Sáb • Sam
	1	2	3	4	5	6
7	8	9	10	11	12	13
14 Valentine's Day	15 President's Day (US)	16	17	18	19	20
21	22	23	24	25	26	27
28						

Marzo • March • Mars

S	M	T	W	T	F	S
	1	2	3	4	5	6
7	8	9	10	11	12	13
14	15	16	17	18	19	20
21	22	23	24	25	26	27
28	29	30	31			

Notes • Notas • Remarques

MARCH | Marzo • Mars

2021

SUNDAY Dom • Dim	MONDAY Lun • Lun	TUESDAY Mar • Mar	WEDNESDAY Mié • Mer	THURSDAY Jue • Jeu	FRIDAY Vie • Jeu	SATURDAY Sáb • Sam
	1	2	3	4	5	6
7	8	9	10	11	12	13
14	15	16	17	18	19	20
Mothers Day (UK) 21	22	23	24 St. Patrick's Day (UK)	25	26	27
28	29	30	31			

Notes • Notas • Remarques

Abril • April • Abvil

S	M	T	W	T	F	S
				1	2	3
4	5	6	7	8	9	10
11	12	13	14	15	16	17
18	19	20	21	22	23	24
25	26	27	28	29	30	

2021

APRIL | Abril • Avril

SUNDAY Dom • Dim	MONDAY Lun • Lun	TUESDAY Mar • Mar	WEDNESDAY Mié • Mer	THURSDAY Jue • Jeu	FRIDAY Vie • Jeu	SATURDAY Sáb • Sam
				1	2	3
4	5	6	7	8	9 Good Friday	10
11	12 Easter Monday (UK)	13	14	15	16	17
18	19	20	21	22	23	24
25	26	27	28	29	30	

Mayo • May • Peut

S	M	T	W	T	F	S
						1
2	3	4	5	6	7	8
9	10	11	12	13	14	15
16	17	18	19	20	21	22
23	24	25	26	27	28	29
30	31					

Notes • Notas • Remarques

2021

MAY | Mayo • Peut

SUNDAY Dom • Dim	MONDAY Lun • Lun	TUESDAY Mar • Mar	WEDNESDAY Mié • Mer	THURSDAY Jue • Jeu	FRIDAY Vie • Jeu	SATURDAY Sáb • Sam
						1
2	3	4	5	6	7	8
9 Mother's Day (US, CA)	10 May Day (UK)	11	12	13	14	15
16	17	18	19	20	21	22
23	24 Victoria Day (CA)	25	26	27	28	29
30	31 May Bank Holiday (UK) Memorial Day (US)					

Junio • June • Juin

S	M	T	W	T	F	S
		1	2	3	4	5
6	7	8	9	10	11	12
13	14	15	16	17	18	19
20	21	22	23	24	25	26
27	28	29	30			

Notes • Notas • Remarques

2021

JUNE | Junio • Juin

SUNDAY Dom • Dim	MONDAY Lun • Lun	TUESDAY Mar • Mar	WEDNESDAY Mié • Mer	THURSDAY Jue • Jeu	FRIDAY Vie • Jeu	SATURDAY Sáb • Sam
		1	2	3	4	5
6	7	8	9	10	11	12
13	14	15	16	17	18	19
20	21	22	23	24	25	26
27 Father's Day	28	29	30			

Notes • Notas • Remarques

Julio • July • Juillet

S	M	T	W	T	F	S
				1	2	3
4	5	6	7	8	9	10
11	12	13	14	15	16	17
18	19	20	21	22	23	24
25	26	27	28	29	30	31

JULY | Julio • Juillet

2011

SUNDAY Dom • Dim	MONDAY Lun • Lun	TUESDAY Mar • Mar	WEDNESDAY Mié • Mer	THURSDAY Jue • Jeu	FRIDAY Vie • Jeu	SATURDAY Sáb • Sam
				1 Canada Day (CA)	2	3
4 Independence Day (US)	5	6	7	8	9	10
11	12	13	14	15	16	17
18	19	20	21	22	23	24
25	26	27	28	29	30	31

Notes • Notas • Remarques

Agosto • August • Août

S	M	T	W	T	F	S
	1	2	3	4	5	6	7
8	9	10	11	12	13	14
15	16	17	18	19	20	21
22	23	24	25	26	27	28
29	30	31				

SUNDAY Dom • Dim	MONDAY Lun • Lun	TUESDAY Mar • Mar	WEDNESDAY Mié • Mer	THURSDAY Jue • Jeu	FRIDAY Vie • Jeu	SATURDAY Sáb • Sam
1	2	3	4	5	6	7
8	9	10	11	12	13	14
15	16	17	18	19	20	21
22	23	24	25	26	27	28
29	30	31 August Bank Holiday (UK)				

Notes • Notas • Remarques

Septiembre • September • Septembre

S	M	T	W	T	F	S
				1	2	3	4
5	6	7	8	9	10	11
12	13	14	15	16	17	18
19	20	21	22	23	24	25
26	27	28	29	30		

SEPTEMBER | Septiembre • Septembre

2021

SUNDAY Dom • Dim	MONDAY Lun • Lun	TUESDAY Mar • Mar	WEDNESDAY Mié • Mer	THURSDAY Jue • Jeu	FRIDAY Vie • Jeu	SATURDAY Sáb • Sam
			1	2	3	4
5	6	7	8	9	10	11
12	13 Labor Day (US & CA)	14	15	16	17	18
19	20	21	22	23	24	25
26	27	28	29	30		

Notes • Notas • Remarques

Octubre • October • Octobre

S	M	T	W	T	F	S
					1	2
3	4	5	6	7	8	9
10	11	12	13	14	15	16
17	18	19	20	21	22	23
24	25	26	27	28	29	30
31						

OCTOBER | Octubre • Octubre

2021

SUNDAY Dom • Dim	MONDAY Lun • Lun	TUESDAY Mar • Mar	WEDNESDAY Mié • Mer	THURSDAY Jue • Jeu	FRIDAY Vie • Jeu	SATURDAY Sáb • Sam
					1	2
3	4	5	6	7	8	9
10	11	12	13	14	15	16
17	18 Columbus Day (US) Thanksgiving Day (CA)	19	20	21	22	23
24	25	26	27	28	29	30
31 Halloween						

Notes • Notas • Remarques

Noviembre • November • Novembre

S	M	T	W	T	F	S
	1	2	3	4	5	6
7	8	9	10	11	12	13
14	15	16	17	18	19	20
21	22	23	24	25	26	27
28	29	30				

SUNDAY Dom • Dim	MONDAY Lun • Lun	TUESDAY Mar • Mar	WEDNESDAY Mié • Mer	THURSDAY Jue • Jeu	FRIDAY Vie • Jeu	SATURDAY Sáb • Sam
	1	2	3	4	5	6
7	8	9	10	11	12	13
14	15	16	17	18 Veterans Day (US) Remembrance Day (CA)	19	20
21	22	23	24	25 Thanksgiving Day (US)	26	27
28	29	30				

Notes • Notas • Remarques

Diciembre • December • Décembre

S	M	T	W	T	F	S
			1	2	3	4
5	6	7	8	9	10	11
12	13	14	15	16	17	18
19	20	21	22	23	24	25
26	27	28	29	30	31	

DECEMBER | Diciembre • Décembre

2021

SUNDAY Dom • Dim	MONDAY Lun • Lun	TUESDAY Mar • Mar	WEDNESDAY Mié • Mer	THURSDAY Jue • Jeu	FRIDAY Vie • Jeu	SATURDAY Sáb • Sam
			1	2	3	4
5	6	7	8	9	10	11
12	13	14	15	16	17	18
19	20	21	22	23	24	25 Christmas Day (US & CA)
26 Boxing Day	27 Christmas Holiday (UK)	28 Boxing Day Holiday UK)	29	30	31	

Notes • Notas • Remarques

Enero • January • Janvier

S	M	T	W	T	F	S
						1
2	3	4	5	6	7	8
9	10	11	12	13	14	15
16	17	18	19	20	21	22
23	24	25	26	27	28	29
30	31					

Notes

2021

Notas • Remarques

2021 Notes

Notas • Remarques

Made in the USA
Monee, IL
15 December 2021

85580719R00017

Saturn is the sixth planet from the sun.
A mysterious planet to everyone.

Lucy exclaimed "Uranus, we're next to see you!
What an icy planet, a colour of pale blue."

Uranus rotates 'round the sun on its side!
Wouldn't that produce an interesting ride?

Of all the planets, it has the stinkiest smell –
Like icky rotten eggs stuck down a well.

·The first planet found with a telescope:
Uranus gave astronomers hope.

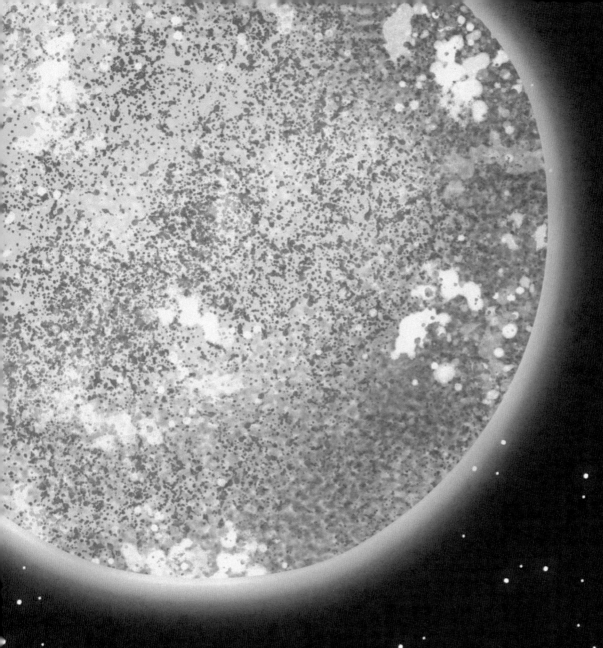

"Don't worry dog, we'll be there soon!"
Luna Lucy said to her pooch Neptune.

"To the next planet we go — your special name,
My favourite planet, I proclaim!

With 13 moons and a shade so blue,
A planet that always reminds me of you."

Neptune is dark, windy and cold, where a day is only 16 hours old.

WOOF! WOOF!

There is one more planet, so tiny, so small,
Some people say it isn't a planet at all.

Once named the planet ninth from the sun. Pluto is now dwarf planet number one.

"I think we better head home soon,"
Lucy yawned as they flew past the moon."

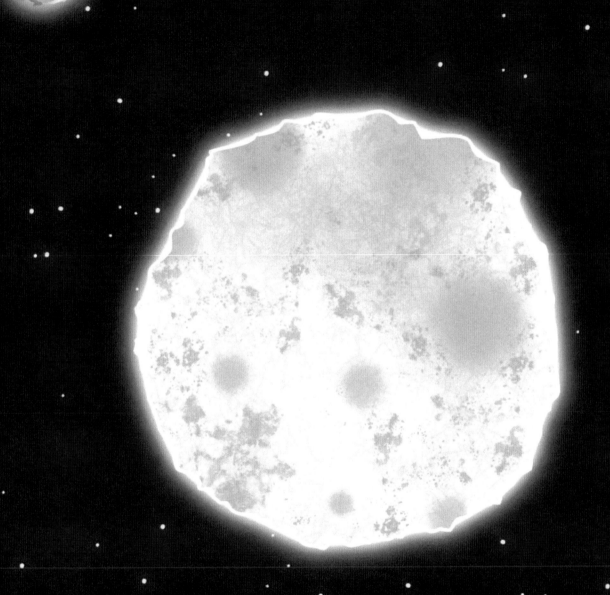

They landed safely in their cardboard box.
Snuggled up in pyjamas and socks.

Just before they hit the ground, you couldn't hear a single sound.
For Lucy and Neptune were fast asleep –
Dreaming of planets and jumping sheep.

Z

Z

Z

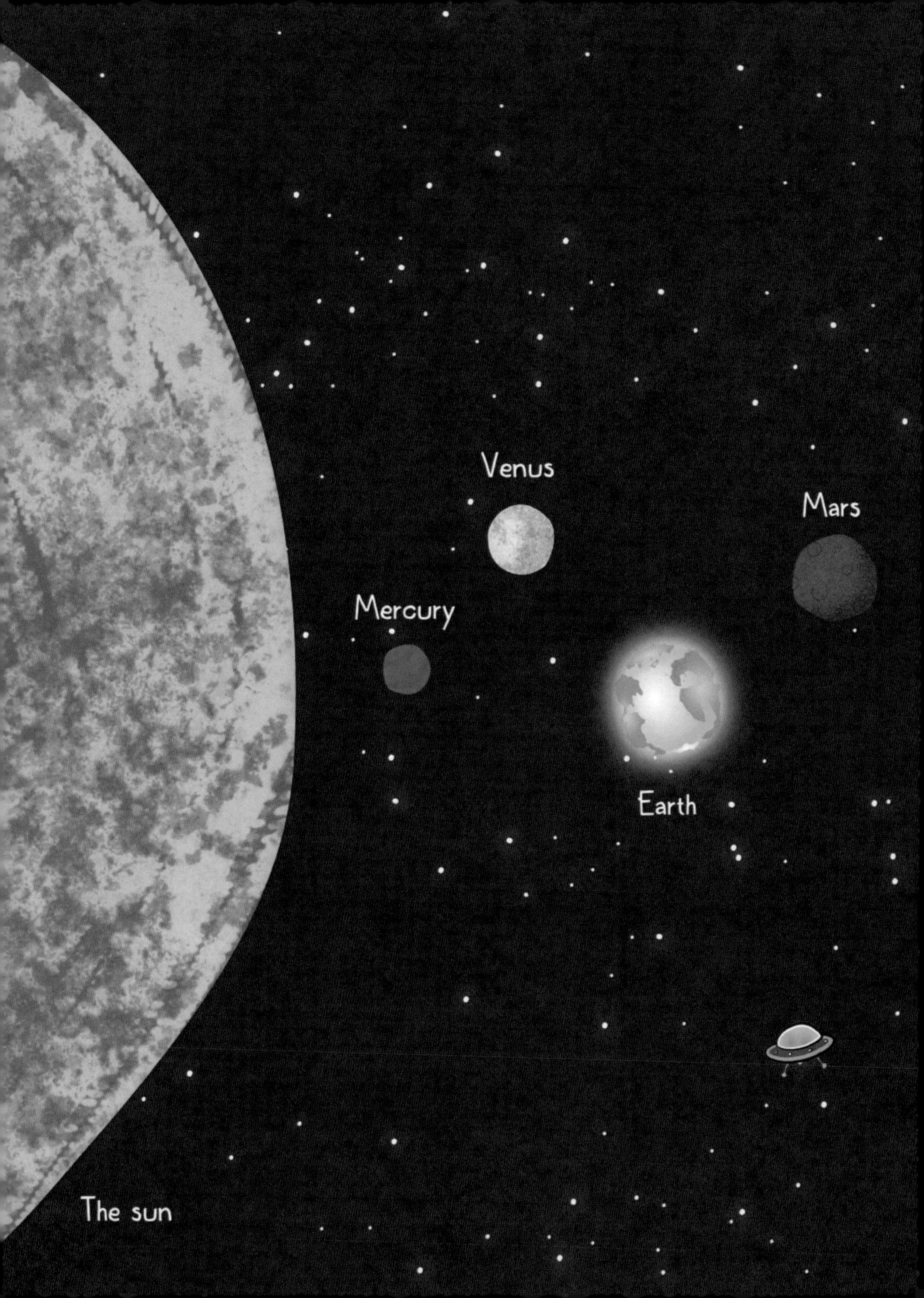
Venus
Mars
Mercury
Earth
The sun

Jupiter

Uranus

Pluto

Saturn

Neptune

Made in the USA
Monee, IL
15 December 2021

85656247R00019